JOHN TAVENER

CHORAL MUSIC
FOR UPPER VOICES

selected and edited by Barry Rose

CONTENTS

CHESTER MUSIC

part of The Music Sales Group
14/15 Berners Street, London W1T 3LJ
tel: +44 (0)20 7612 7400 fax: +44 (0)20 7612 7549
Exclusive distributor: Music Sales Limited,
Newmarket Road, Bury St Edmunds, Suffolk, IP33 3YB
tel: +44 (0)1284 702600 fax: +44 (0)1284 702592
web: www.chesternovello.com e-mail: music@musicsales.co.uk

COMPOSER'S NOTE

I am delighted to introduce this collection of original pieces for upper voices and arrangements by Barry Rose of some of my best-known works for mixed choir. Beginning with *The Lamb* from 1982, and including settings of *The Lord's Prayer* in French and English and *Song for Athene*, I hope that there will be something here for all abilities and combinations of upper voices to enjoy.

J.T.

The Lamb (1982)
arranged for upper voices by Barry Rose
Text by William Blake (1757–1827)

First performed on 24th December 1982 by the Choir of King's College, Cambridge, as part of A Festival of Nine Lessons and Carols.

Duration: c. 3 minutes
The original version for unaccompanied choir SATB is also available: Order No. CH55570

The Lord's Prayer (1999)
arranged for upper voices and piano/organ by Barry Rose
Text from The Bible (Matthew 6, vv 9–13)

Commissioned by the Guildford Philharmonic for the Tallis Scholars, with assistance from South East Arts. First performed on 10th March 2000 by the Tallis Scholars, at Holy Trinity Church, Guildford.

The composer writes: "This setting of *The Lord's Prayer* should be sung very quietly, with an inner serenity and calm that is almost 'silent'. This is the Prayer of all Prayers, and nothing can violate its silent theophany."

Duration: c. 2 minutes
The original version for unaccompanied choir SATB is also available: Order No. CH61706

Notre Père (1996)
The Lord's Prayer
Text from The Bible (Matthew 6, vv 9–13)

Commissioned by Les Petits Chanteurs de Saint-André de Colmar, and first performed by them on 1st June 1997.

Duration: c. 3 minutes

Song for Athene (1993)
arranged for upper voices and organ, with optional cello, by Barry Rose
Text from Shakespeare's *Hamlet*, and from the Orthodox Funeral Service

Commissioned by the BBC, and first performed on 22nd January 1994 at St Giles' Church, Cripplegate, London, by the BBC Singers conducted by Simon Joly.

This work was written in memory of Athene Hariades, who died tragically in March 1993. Her inner and outer beauty was reflected in her love of acting, poetry, music and of the Orthodox Church. *Song for Athene* became well known after it was performed at the funeral of Diana, Princess of Wales in 1997. If the work is to be performed at the funeral of a man, the word 'servant' may be substituted for 'hand-maid' in bar 14.

Duration: c. 7 minutes
The original version for unaccompanied choir SATB is also available: Order No. CH60991

Awed by the Beauty (2005)
from *The Veil of the Temple* (2002)
arranged for upper voices and organ by Barry Rose
Byzantine text translated by Mother Thekla

The all-night vigil *The Veil of the Temple* was commissioned by the Temple Music Trust. The world premiere took place on 27th June 2003, in the Temple Church, London, performed by the Choir of the Temple Church and the Holst Singers, with Patricia Rozario (soprano), conducted by Stephen Layton, as part of The City of London Festival, 2003. The anthem *Awed by the Beauty* was arranged for unaccompanied choir SATB by the composer in 2005.

Duration: c. 2 minutes
The original anthem for unaccompanied choir SATB is available in *Five Anthems from The Veil of the Temple:* Order No. CH73656

Agnus Dei
from *Missa Brevis* (2005)

Missa Brevis was commissioned by Westminster Cathedral. It was first performed on 28th June 2005, at Westminster Cathedral, London, by Westminster Cathedral Choir conducted by Martin Baker. The work is dedicated to His Holiness Pope John Paul II.

Duration: c. 2½ minutes

Missa Brevis was originally written for treble voices (with organ in the *Gloria* and *Sanctus*). It is available on sale: Order No. CH69971. A version for mixed chorus and organ is also available: Order No. CH70400

Theotóke (2001)

Commissioned by London ArtFest. First performed on 31st October 2001 at Middle Temple Hall, London, by the Moscow Youth Choir conducted by Anna Vedrova.

The Greek word Θεοτόκε literally means 'God-bearer', and this short piece is an invocation to the Mother of God. The music should be sung with vigour, preferably in a resonant acoustic.

Duration: c. 3 minutes

Ikon of Saint Hilda (1998)
Text by Mother Thekla

Commissioned by Joan Branton for Louise Marsh and the Girls' Choir of Wakefield Cathedral, and first performed at Wakefield Cathedral on 27th June 1999.

The text by Mother Thekla, former abbess of the Orthodox Monastery of the Assumption, Normanby, near Whitby, is framed by an Alliuatic Antiphon. It is a tribute to St Hilda, seventh-century abbess and scholar, and leader of a double monastery of both monks and nuns. She knew and encouraged the writer Caedman, and she presided over the Synod of Whitby, at which the British Church agreed how the date of Easter should be calculated.

Duration: c. 6 minutes

Performance Note
♯, ♭ and ♮ represent microtones, the characteristic 'breaks in the voice' of Eastern chant.

Order No. CH75735   ISBN 978-1-84938-239-7

Cover design by Fresh Lemon

for Simon's 3rd birthday

1. THE LAMB

John Tavener
arr. Barry Rose

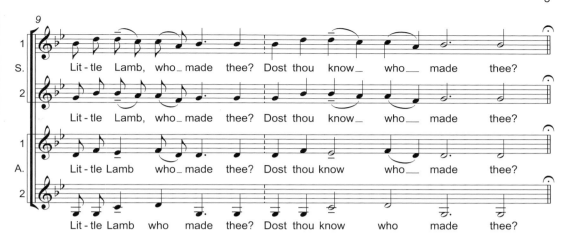

Lit - tle Lamb, who_ made thee? Dost thou know_ who_ made thee?

Lit - tle Lamb, who_ made thee? Dost thou know_ who_ made thee?

Lit - tle Lamb who_ made thee? Dost thou know who_ made thee?

Lit - tle Lamb who made thee? Dost thou know who made thee?

A tempo – moving forward

Lit - tle Lamb, I'll_ tell thee, Lit - tle Lamb, I'll_ tell thee;

Lit - tle Lamb, I'll_ tell thee, Lit - tle Lamb, I'll_ tell thee;

Lit - tle Lamb, I'll_ tell thee;

Lit - tle Lamb, I'll_ tell thee;

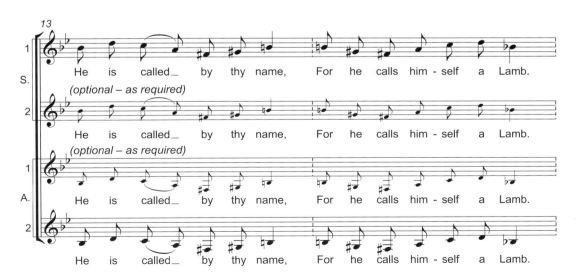

He is called_ by thy name, For he calls him - self a Lamb.

(optional – as required)

He is called_ by thy name, For he calls him - self a Lamb.

(optional – as required)

He is called_ by thy name, For he calls him - self a Lamb.

He is called_ by thy name, For he calls him - self a Lamb.

4

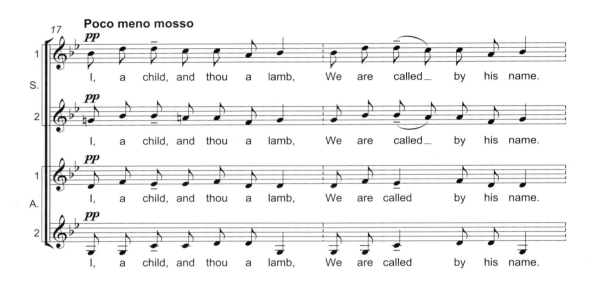

for the birth of Charlotte

2. THE LORD'S PRAYER
(1999)

John Tavener
arr. Barry Rose

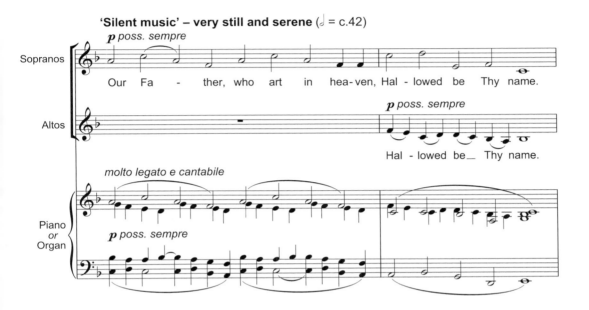

6

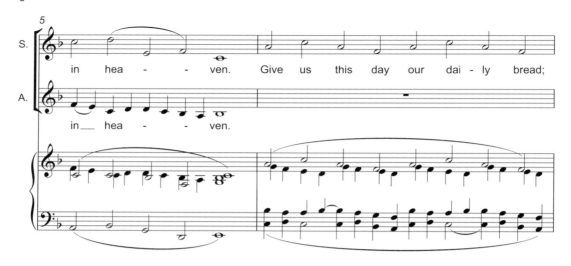

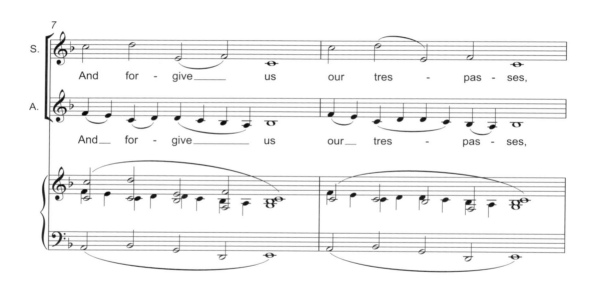

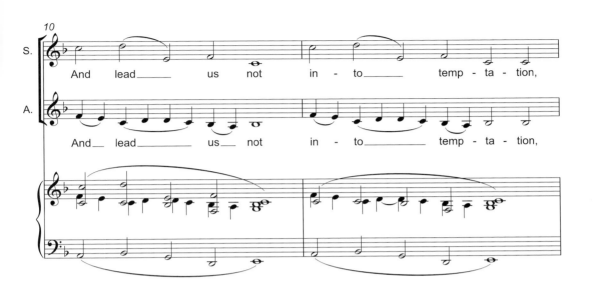

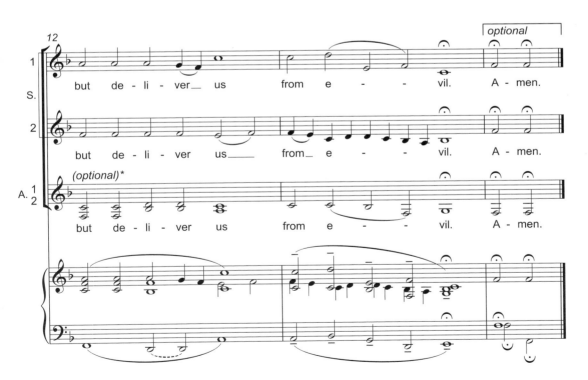

* If the optional alto parts are not sung, all sopranos should sing the S.1 line, and all altos the S.2 part.

for the baptism of Sofia
and for Les Petits Chanteurs de Saint-André de Colmar

3. NOTRE PÈRE

John Tavener

* This piece may also be sung in English, but performance in French is preferred.
† See Preface

4. SONG FOR ATHENE

for upper voices, organ and optional cello

John Tavener
arr. Barry Rose

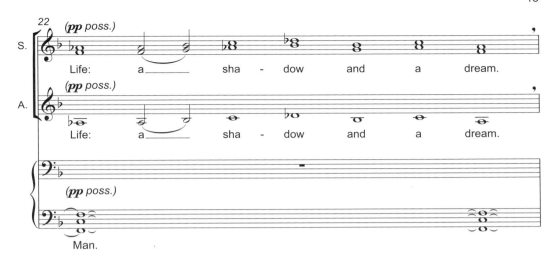

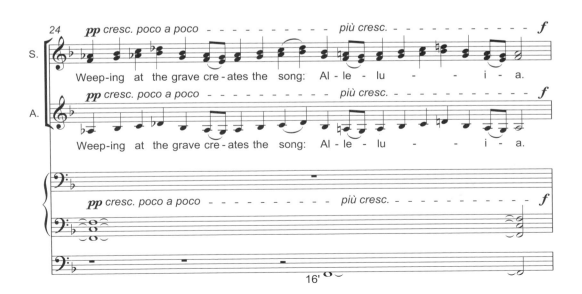

With resplendent joy in the Resurrection

*'Oh.' as in the 'o' of log. Breathe when necessary, but not simultaneously.

5. AWED BY THE BEAUTY

from *The Veil of the Temple*

John Tavener
arr. Barry Rose

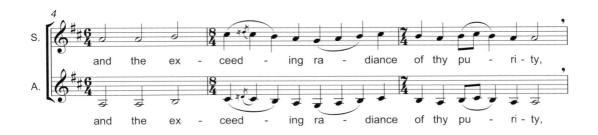

† See Preface
* If this part is played on the piano (or other keyboard), use the sustaining pedal
and repeat tied chords as necessary.

© Copyright 2005, 2009 Chester Music Ltd.

A little slower

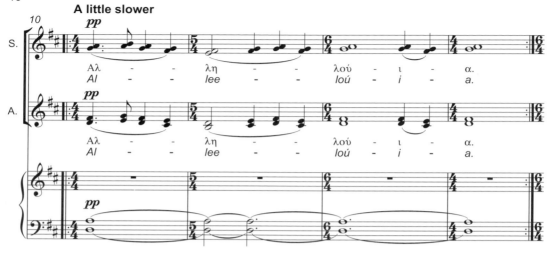

Tempo I
With ecstatic breath (♩ = c.88)

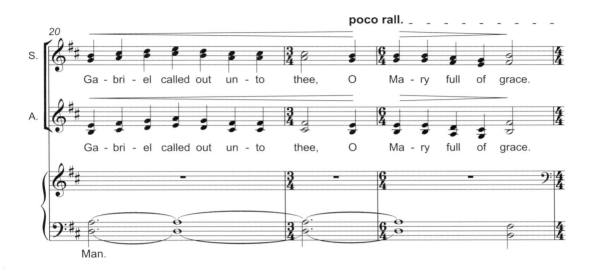

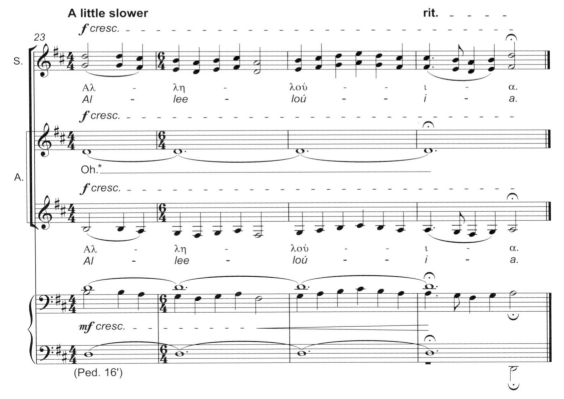

* 'Oh' as in the 'o' of 'log'. Breathe when necessary, but not simultaneously.

6. AGNUS DEI

from *Missa Brevis*

John Tavener

7. ΘΕΟΤΟΚΕ
Theotóke

John Tavener

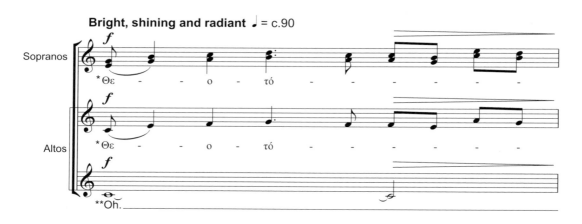

* Θεοτόκε: Θε as in English <u>the</u>spian; ο as in <u>top</u>; τό as in <u>top</u>; κε as in <u>kept</u>.

** 'Oh' as in the 'o' of log. Breathe when necessary, but not simultaneously.

† See Preface

for Louise Marsh and the Girls Choir of Wakefield Cathedral

8. IKON OF SAINT HILDA

John Tavener

Strong and rhythmic
in Byzantine style (♩ = c.60, ♪ = c.120)

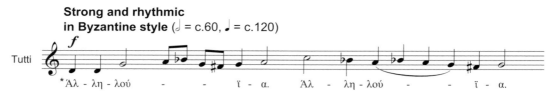

*The Greek word Ἀλληλούϊα should be pronounced 'Alleeloueeya':
Ἀ as in the 'a' of French 'la'; λλη 'lee'; λού 'lou'; ϊ 'ee'; α 'ya' with short 'a', as in French 'la'.

* 'Oh' as in the 'o' of log. Breathe when necessary, but not simultaneously.

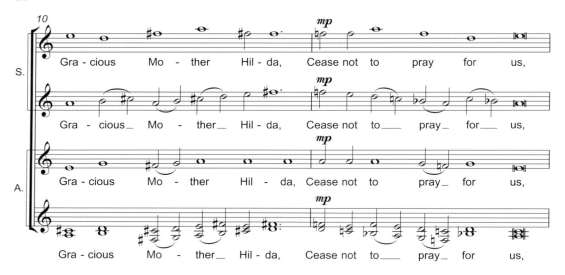

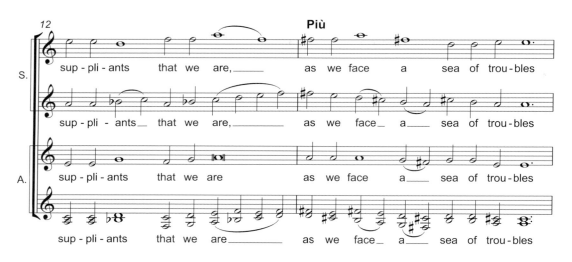

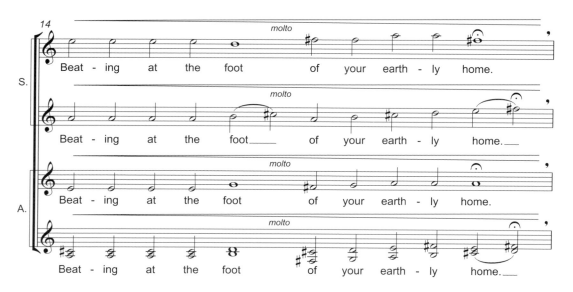

* If there are insufficient voices to sing all the parts in this section, some notes in each chord could be
  discreetly covered by a suitable keyboard instrument.
† See Preface

Still, like the breath of the Spirit ($\bold{\quad}$ = c.52)

You are a sweet and fra-grant es - sence, And— rock for a strong-hold of Faith,

Ah._____

Ah._____

A____ mo - ther of nuns of all a - ges, So too of bi - shops and monks:

(Ah.)_____

(Ah.)_____

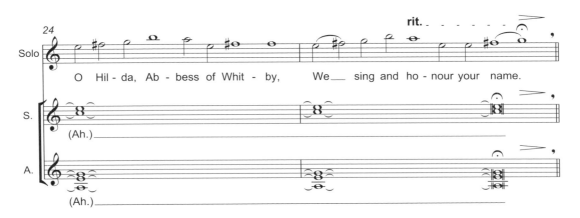

O Hil - da, Ab - bess of Whit - by, We__ sing and ho - nour your name.

(Ah.)_____

(Ah.)_____

*If necessary, this solo may be sung an octave lower.
In this case, omit the highest soprano note (E) in the sustained chord.

30

Strong and rhythmic
in Byzantine style (♩ = c.60, ♪ = c.120)

Ἀλ - λη - λού - - ϊ - α. Ἀλ - λη - λού - - ϊ - α.

Ἀλ - λη - λού - - ϊ - α. Ἀλ - λη - λού - ϊ - α. Ἀλ - λη -

λού - - - - ϊ - α. Ἀλ - λη - λού - ϊ - α. Ἀλ -

-λη - λού - ϊ - α. Ἀλ - λη - λού - ϊ - α. Ἀλ - λη - λού - - ϊ - α. Ἀλ - λη -

λού - - ϊ - α. Ἀλ - λη - λού - - - ϊ - α. Ἀλ - λη -

rit.

λού - - (ού) (ού) (ού) - ϊ - α. Ἀλ - λη - λού - - ϊ - α.

1 2 3 4 5 6 7 8 9